Dav the Donkey™

Andrew McDonough

Dave the donkey was so excited. He'd been watching all week for Grandpa donkey to get back from Jerusalem. Dave had some big news he'd been waiting to share with him.

"Grandpa! Grandpa! Guess what? I carried the king into Jerusalem."

"You're joking, Dave."
"No, Grandpa. I carried the king!"

"I was standing out the front, minding my own business, when the king's servant untied me and led me to the king.

The king jumped on my back and . . .

we charged down the hill and up the mountain to Jerusalem.

The crowd waved palm branches and everyone cheered, 'Hooray for the king! Long live the king!'

We said goodbye, and I headed home leaving the king to get on with the job of being king.

So, Grandpa, you've been in Jerusalem since then, tell me what happened next. Did the crowd keep cheering for the king?"

"Well, Dave, the crowd were yelling for the king."

"Wow!" said Dave,
"And I'm sure all the leaders
came to meet him."

"Yes," sighed Grandpa,
"the king did meet
all the leaders."

"And, Grandpa, they would have placed a golden crown upon the king's head."

"They certainly crowned the king, but the crown wasn't made of gold."

"The throne, Grandpa, they must have led the king into the palace, sat him on the throne and cheered, 'Long live the king!'"

Dave was stunned.

"A cross? So . . . so the king . . . the king is dead."

"No, Dave. The king was dead. The king was placed in a tomb and the tomb was sealed with a heavy stone.

Dave stared across the valley to Jerusalem, as the strange and wonderful news rolled through his mind, "The king was dead, but now he is alive."

"Grandpa," asked Dave, "did you ever carry someone special that you will never forget?"

"Yes, Dave," said Grandpa, "as a matter of fact I did. It was long ago on a starry night like this. I carried someone special that I will never forget.

Long live the king, Dave! Long live the king."

Cecil's Page

Hi Friends,

Dave the Donkey is based on the account of Jesus entering Jerusalem in Mark 11:1—10 and the strange and wonderful story of his death and resurrection found in each of the Gospels. In this story, you're the older, wiser, slightly wrinklier one who knows more about the rough and tumble of life and the events of Easter. This story gives you a chance to discuss issues with your child like hope, sin, death and salvation. Relax, Grandpa donkey probably didn't have all the answers, you won't need to either.

This story isn't just for Easter. The cross, the resurrection and the good news that Jesus is still the king is worth celebrating everyday of the year.

Before the story

A good place to start is by asking your child what they like about Easter. Tell them this is a story of what happened at the first Easter.

Read the story

After the story

Maybe your child has asked you questions during this story. If they have, just go with the flow. If not, here are a few questions you may like to ask: "Why was Dave so excited?", "Who was the king?", "Why was Dave stunned?", "What was Grandpa so excited about?" This is still the exciting news — Jesus is alive today and he is the king. Help your child grasp this and you help them take the first steps in a life of faith.

God's blessing,
Cecil

(N.B. A way to help children connect Easter and Christmas is by asking,
"Can you guess who the woman was that Grandpa carried when he was young?")

Mark 11:1-10 (CEV)

Jesus and his disciples reached Bethphage and Bethany near the Mount of Olives. When they were getting close to Jerusalem, Jesus sent two of them on ahead. He told them, "Go into the next village. As soon as you enter it, you'll find a young donkey that has never been ridden. Untie the donkey and bring it here. If anyone asks why you're doing that, say, 'The Lord needs it and will soon bring it back.'"

The disciples left and found the donkey tied near a door that faced the street. While they were untying it some of the people standing there asked, "Why are you untying the donkey?" They told them what Jesus had said, and the people let them take it.

The disciples led the donkey to Jesus. They put some of their clothes on its back, and Jesus got on. Many people spread clothes on the road, while others went to cut branches from the fields.

In front of Jesus and behind him, people went along shouting, "Hooray! God bless the one who comes in the name of the Lord! God bless the coming kingdom of our ancestor David. Hooray for God in heaven above!"

First printing February 2008
17 16 15 14 13 12   10 9 8 7 6 5 4 3

National Library of Australia
Cataloguing-in-Publication entry

Author:	McDonough, Andrew (Andrew John)
Title:	Dave the donkey : an Easter story / Andrew McDonough.
Publisher:	Unley, S. Aust. : Lost Sheep Resources, 2008.
ISBN:	9781921229268 (pbk.)
Target Audience:	For primary school age.
Subjects:	Bible. N.T. Mark I, 1-10--Juvenile literature.
	Easter stories.
	Bible stories, English--Juvenile literature.
	Picture books for children.
Dewey Number:	226.3

Dave's Life Coach: Stewart Bogle
Stable cleaners: The WestCare Daves

Dave is happy to appear in nativity plays and Palm Sunday processions but draws the line at children's parties.

Designed and published by Lost Sheep
Distributed by Authentic Media in partnership with Lost Sheep
Printed in Singapore by Tien Wah Press Pte Ltd
Authentic Media, 52 Presley Way, CrownHill, Milton Keynes, MK8 0ES, United Kingdom
Lost Sheep, PO Box 3191, Unley SA 5061, Australia
info@lostsheep.com.au
lostsheep.com.au